EASA Private Pilot Licence & Light Aircraft Pilot Licence
Aeroplane & Helicopter
Communications Revision Guide

ISBN 9781 906559 571

Airplan Flight Equipment

This book is intended to be a study aid to the Communications Theoretical Knowledge element of the EASA PPL and LAPL (A & H) courses. It does not in any way replace or overrule the instruction you will receive from a flight instructor at an approved or registered training organisation.

Nothing in this publication overrules or supersedes EASA regulations or EU rules and other documents published by a competent authority; the flight manual/pilot's operating handbook for the aircraft being flown; the pilot order book or operations manual; training syllabus; or the general provisions of good airmanship and safe flying practice.

First Edition 2013

Revised Edition 2015

This Revised Edition 2017

©Copyright 2013, 2015 & 2017 AFE Ltd.

EASA Private Pilot Licence & Light Aircraft Pilot Licence
Aeroplane & Helicopter
Communications Revision Guide

ISBN 9781 906559 571

Airplan Flight Equipment
1a Ringway Trading Estate
Shadowmoss Road
Manchester M22 5LH
Tel: 0161 499 0023
Fax: 0161 499 0298
www.afeonline.com

CONTENTS

Intentionally Left Blank

Definitions

The following **spoken abbreviations** are common:

Abbreviation	Meaning
ATIS*	Automatic Terminal Information Service (pronounced "Ay-tis")
ATC	Air Traffic Control (in general)
ATZ	Aerodrome Traffic Zone
CAVOK*	Visibility, cloud and present weather better than certain prescribed conditions (pronounced "Cav-okay")
CB*	Cumulo Nimbus (pronounced "Cee-bee")
DF	Direction Finding
ETA	Estimated Time of Arrival
FIR	Flight Information Region
FIS	Flight Information Service
IFR	Instrument Flight Rules
IMC	Instrument Meteorological Conditions
LARS*	Lower Airspace Radar Service
MATZ*	Military Aerodrome Traffic Zone
MET*	Meteorology or Meteorological
PAPI*	Precision Approach Path Indicator
POB	Persons On Board
QDM	A magnetic track to a point (eg a heading to steer assuming zero wind)
QFE	The altimeter pressure setting to indicate height (above a fixed point on the surface)
QNH	The altimeter pressure setting to indicate altitude (above mean sea level)
SSR	Secondary Surveillance Radar
TCAS	Terminal Alert and Collision Avoidance System (pronounced "Tee-Kas")
TMA	Terminal Control Area
UHF	Ultra High Frequency (used at military airfields)
UTC	Co-ordinated Universal Time
VASI*	Visual Approach Slope Indicator (pronounced "Var-Zi")
VDF	VHF Direction Finding
VFR	Visual Flight Rules
VMC	Visual Meteorological Conditions
VOLMET*	Meteorological information for aircraft in flight

* These abbreviations tend to be spoken as a single word.

The **order of precedence** for radio messages, starting with the most important, is:

1. Distress messages
2. Urgency messages
3. Direction Finding messages
4. Flight Safety messages
5. Meteorological messages
6. Flight Regularity messages

An aircraft may only abbreviate its call sign after an ATSU has done so. The main **call sign abbreviations** are:

Call sign	Abbreviation
Aircraft registration	First and last two letters of registration
Operator Designator and registration	Operator designator and last two letters of registration
Aircraft type and registration	Aircraft type and last two letters of registration
Operator Designator and flight identification	NO ABBREVIATION PERMITTED
Aircraft type only	NO ABBREVIATION PERMITTED

General Operating Procedures

The **ATSU call signs** are:

Type of ATSU	Call sign
Air Traffic Control Unit	Approach, Control, Director, Ground, Radar, Tower
Aerodrome Flight Information Service (AFIS)	Information
Aerodrome Air/Ground Communications Service	Radio

It is normal practice to drop the name, call sign and suffix of the Air Traffic Service Unit (or ground station) once satisfactory two-way communication has been established, and where there will be no confusion.

A **departure clearance** describes the routing to be followed after take-off. A departure clearance is not a clearance to take-off. A pilot ready to take-off should report 'ready for departure', and not use the phrase 'take-off' until the ATSU does so.

A **conditional clearance** is given in the format:

Aircraft call sign/the condition/the instruction

A **Special VFR (**SVFR) clearance allows a flight to operate in a control zone (CTR) without complying with Instrument Flight Rules (IFR), but in weather conditions which do not meet the Visual Meteorological Conditions (VMC) criteria specified for that airspace.

MATZ penetration should be requested at least 15nm or 5 minutes flying time before reaching the zone boundary – whichever is greater.

The standard **Secondary Surveillance Radar (SSR)** transponder terminology is:

Squawk [code]	Set this code
Squawk Charlie	Set the transponder to mode C (altitude reporting)
Squawk standby	Set the transponder to the standby position
Squawk ident	Operate the ident button (position identification feature) on the transponder
Confirm squawk [code]	Confirm the code set on the transponder
Reset Squawk [code]	Set the transponder to standby, then re-select the assigned code
Confirm [level]	Check and confirm your level (used to verify the flight level/altitude read-out the controller is seeing)

The **standard transponder codes** are:

7000	The standard conspicuity code, to be used outside controlled airspace if no other code has been allocated to the aircraft
7500	The aircraft is being subject to unlawful interference
7600	The aircraft has experienced a communications failure
7700	The aircraft is in difficulties

In **VHF Direction Finding** (**VDF**) the following 'Q codes' may be used:

QDM	The magnetic track **TO** the VDF station; the magnetic heading for the aircraft to steer to reach the VDF station, assuming no wind.
QDR	The magnetic bearing of the aircraft **FROM** the VDF station, the reciprocal of the QDM.
QTE	The true bearing FROM the VDF station – the QDR corrected for magnetic variation.

VDF information given to an aircraft will be qualified as one of the following classes:

Class A Accuracy ±2°

Class B Accuracy ±5°

Class C Accuracy ±10°

Class D Accuracy less than class C

The standard overhead join:

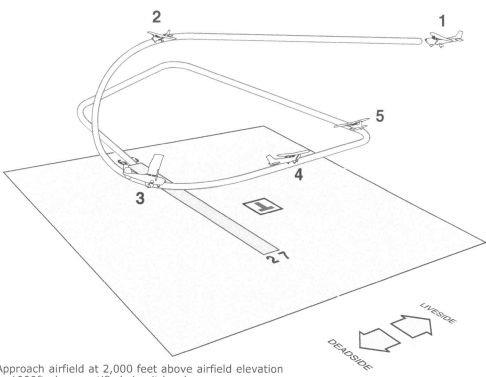

1 Approach airfield at 2,000 feet above airfield elevation or 1000ft above notified circuit level

2 Observe signals square and windsock, determine runway in use. If unable to do so, continue circling. Lookout for other aircraft. Maintain height until on 'deadside' Radio call "Overhead for runway xx"

3 Once on deadside, make a descending turn (in the circuit direction) to circuit height remaining on the deadside. Radio call if required, "Deadside descending"

4 Pass within the upwind end of the runway, level at circuit height

5 Join the circuit, maintain good lookout

Transmissions on the **'SAFETYCOM'** frequency should be made when no more than 2000ft above aerodrome level (or not more than 1000ft above the circuit height) and within 10nm of the airfield.

Transmission of Letters

The **phonetic alphabet**:

Letter	Phonetic Word	Letter	Phonetic Word	Letter	Phonetic Word
A	Alpha	J	Juliett	S	Sierra
B	Bravo	K	Kilo	T	Tango
C	Charlie	L	Lima	U	Uniform
D	Delta	M	Mike	V	Victor
E	Echo	N	November	W	Whiskey
F	Foxtrot	O	Oscar	X	X-ray
G	Golf	P	Papa	Y	Yankee
H	Hotel	Q	Quebec	Z	Zulu
I	India	R	Romeo		

Transmission of Numbers

Number	Pronunciation
0	**ZERO**
1	**WUN**
2	**TOO**
3	**TREE**
4	**FOWER**
5	**FIFE**
6	**SIX**
7	**SEVEN**
8	**AIT**
9	**NINER**
Decimal	**DAYSEEMAL**
Hundred	**HUN DRED**
Thousand	**TOUSAND**

Numbers are transmitted as separate digits in the following cases: aircraft call signs; altimeter settings; flight levels, headings, wind speed/direction; transponder codes; radio frequencies.

When a **radio frequency is transmitted**, the word 'decimal' is used.

Numbers containing hundreds or thousands are transmitted using the digits of the number together with the word HUN DRED or TOUSAND in these instances: altitude; cloud ceiling; cloud height; height.

Transmission of Time

When **time is transmitted**, just the minutes past the hour are used unless there may be confusion. Time is always given in UTC, using the 24 hour clock.

Transmission Technique

Standard Phraseology:

Word/Phrase	Meaning
Acknowledge	Confirm that you have received and understood this message
Affirm	Yes (shortened from affirmative)
Approved	Permission for proposed action is granted
Break	This is a separation between messages
Break Break	Indicates a separation between messages in a busy RTF environment
Cancel	Annul the previously transmitted clearance
Changing to	I intend to call (unit) on (frequency)
Check	Examine a system or procedure
Cleared	Authorised to proceed under the conditions specified
Climb	Climb and maintain
Confirm	I request verification of (message/information)? Did you correctly receive this message?
Confirm squawk (code)	Confirm the code and mode you have set on the transponder
Contact	Establish radio contact with (unit), (they have your details)
Correct	True or Accurate
Correction	An error has been made. The correct message is…
Descend	Descend and maintain
Disregard	Ignore
Fanstop	I am initiating a practice engine failure after take-off
Freecall	Call (ATSU), (they do not have your details)
How do you read?	What is the readability of my transmissions?
I Say Again	I will repeat (for clarity or emphasis)
Maintain	Continue in accordance with condition specified
Monitor	Listen out on (frequency)
Negative	No, or That is not correct, or Permission is not granted
Out	This exchange is ended and no response is expected
Over	This transmission is ended and I expect a response
Pass your message	Proceed with your message
Read Back	Repeat all, or a specified part, of the message; exactly as you received it
Report	Pass requested information
Request	I want to know, or I want to obtain
Roger	I have received all of your last transmission
Say Again	Repeat all, or a specified part, of your last transmission
Speak Slower	Slow down your rate of speaking
Squawk	Set this mode and code (code and mode)
Squawk Charlie	Set the transponder to mode C
Squawk ident	Operate the ident button on the transponder
Squawk standby	Set the transponder to the standby position
Standby	Wait and I will call you
Unable	I cannot comply with your request, instruction or clearance (a reason is normally given)
Wilco	I understand your message and will co-operate with it
Words Twice	As a request – please transmit each word twice As information – I will transmit each word twice

Items that must be **read back**:

1	Runway in use
2	Clearance to land/take-off/backtrack, cross, enter, or hold short of, an active runway
3	Altimeter Settings
4	Airways, route and approach clearances
5	Taxy instructions
6	Level instructions
7	Heading instructions
8	Speed instructions
9	VDF information
10	Frequency changes
11	Type of radar service
12	SSR (transponder) operating instructions
13	Transition levels
14	Approach clearances

And any other message, item or instruction if an ATSU requests a read back

The readability of aircraft transmissions can be graded as:

Readability Scale	Definition
1	Unreadable
2	Readable now and then
3	Readable but with difficulty
4	Readable
5	Perfectly readable

Weather Information

Automatic Terminal Information Service (**ATIS**) is a continuous broadcast of recorded information for a specific airport, including weather, runway in use, NOTAM and ATC information.

VOLMET is a recorded broadcast of meteorological information for a number of airfields, intended to be received by aircraft in flight. In practice, VOLMET is a recorded broadcast of METARs, normally broadcast in alphabetical order and covering a specific geographical region.

Communication Failure

In general, the best response to a suspected radio failure is to start by checking the frequency in use and attempting to make contact on different frequencies or with nearby aircraft. This may be followed by fault finding of the aircraft equipment (including the headset) before considering whether to squawk 7600 and whether it will be necessary to land at a different airfield than the intended destination.

Distress and Urgency Procedures

Distress: The aircraft is threatened by serious and/or imminent danger and requires immediate assistance. Spoken word **MAYDAY**

A distress (Mayday) message takes priority over *all other radio messages.*

Urgency: A condition concerning the safety of an aircraft or other vehicle, or of some person on board or in sight, but not requiring immediate assistance. Spoken word **PAN PAN**

An urgency (Pan Pan) message takes priority over *all messages except a distress message.*

An emergency radio call should initially be made on the radio frequency in use. If the pilot cannot make contact, or if no frequency is currently in use, the pilot should use the international distress frequency 121.5MHz.

The standard format of an emergency message is:

1   **MAYDAY, MAYDAY, MAYDAY** for distress
    or
    PAN PAN, PAN PAN, PAN PAN for urgency

2   Name of the **station addressed**

3   Aircraft **call sign**

4   Aircraft **Type**

5   **Nature** of emergency

6   **Intentions** of pilot

7   **Position** (or last known position); Flight Level/Altitude/Height; Heading

8   **Pilot qualifications** (eg No instrument qualification, IMC rating etc.)

9   Any other **useful information** (eg persons on board etc.)

General Principles of VHF Propagation

The higher an aircraft flies, the greater the range of VHF communications, VHF communication range is considered to work on the **'line of sight'** principle.

The Very High Frequency (VHF) band is in the **30 – 300MHz** frequency range. VHF frequencies are mostly (but not entirely) unaffected at atmospheric conditions.

Intentionally Left Blank

EASA Private Pilot Licence &
Light Aircraft Pilot Licence
Aeroplane & Helicopter
Communications

Time allowed: 20 minutes
No. of questions: 12
Total Marks: 100

Instructions:

The paper consists of 12 multiple choice questions. The pass mark is 75% (ie 9 questions or more must be answered correctly). Marks are not deducted for incorrect answers.

Be sure to carefully read each question and ensure that you understand it before considering the answer choices. Only one of the answers is complete and correct; the others are either incomplete, incorrect or based on a misconception.

You should indicate the correct answer by placing a cross in the appropriate box of the answer sheet. If you decide to change an answer, you should erase the original choice and put a cross in the box representing your new selection.

Each question has an average answer time available of 1 minute 40 seconds. No credit is given for unanswered questions.

1. How would a radio transmission that is readable, but with difficulty, be classified?

   (a) Readability 5

   (b) Readability 2

   (c) Readability 4

   (d) Readability 3

2. In response to an ATC query "(aircraft call sign) are you visual with the field?", the correct response may use which of following phrases?

   (a) ALMOST, BUT NOT YET

   (b) ROGER

   (c) CORRECT

   (d) AFFIRM or NEGATIVE

3. An aircraft's call-sign may be abbreviated by the pilot:

   (a) Only after it has been abbreviated by the ATSU

   (b) At the pilot's discretion

   (c) In any ongoing RTF exchange

   (d) Never

4. A radio frequency of 118.6MHz should be transmitted as:

   (a) WUN WUN AIT SIX

   (b) WUN WUN AIT DAYSEEMAL SIX

   (c) WUN WUN AIT POINT SIX

   (d) EIGHTEEN DAYSEEMAL SIX

5. The ATSU instruction to check and confirm the aircraft's level, for the purposes of verifying the Mode C transponder altitude information the controller is seeing, is:

   (a) [Call sign] squawk ident

   (b) [Call sign] confirm Mode C readout

   (c) [Call sign] confirm your level

   (d) [Call sign] squawk Charlie

6. During the en-route phase of a flight, in response to the invitation to "Pass your message", the most appropriate reply would include:

   (a) Call sign and type; altitude/level; pilot qualifications; Request

   (b) Call sign and type; departure, current position; next reporting point; persons on board

   (c) Call sign; current position; altitude/level; endurance; flight plan time to destination

   (d) Call sign and type; departure and destination, current position; altitude/level; intentions and flight rules; request

7. It is recommended that transmissions on the SAFETYCOM frequency should be made no more than ..... above the airfield level and within .... of the airfield addressed.

(a) 2000ft, 10nm

(b) 1000ft, 20nm

(c) 10,000ft, 30nm

(d) 3000ft, 15nm

8. A pilot has been passed, acknowledged and has set a QFE altimeter pressure setting. As long as this pressure setting is in use, what term should be used to refer to the aircraft's level?

(a) Altitude

(b) Flight Level

(c) Height

(d) Any of the above, at the pilot's discretion

9. A pilot in contact with a VDF station wishes to obtain the aircraft's true bearing from the station. The request should include the appropriate 'Q' code, which in this case will be:

(a) QDR

(b) QDM

(c) QUJ

(d) QTE

10. To request a MATZ crossing, it is recommended that the pilot should contact the relevant ATSU:

(a) At least 15nm or 5 minutes from the MATZ boundary (whichever is sooner)

(b) No more than 15nm or 5 minutes from the MATZ boundary (whichever is later)

(c) At any time before reaching the MATZ boundary

(d) At the MATZ boundary

11. The correct call-sign prefix to indicate that the pilot is a student pilot flying solo is:

(a) Novice

(b) Solo

(c) Learner

(d) Student

12. The recognised classifications of Emergency Message are:

(a) Hazard, Jeopardy

(b) Distress, Urgency

(c) Threat, Error

(d) Peril, Abnormal

1. A pilot wishing to indicate that he/she has received all of the last transmission should use the phrase:

    (a)   WILCO

    (b)   OVER

    (c)   ROGER

    (d)   CORRECT

2. The phrase 'Disregard' means:

    (a)   An error has been made in the last but one transmission

    (b)   Repeat your last transmission

    (c)   Ignore

    (d)   Cannot comply

3. If the number 4500 is used in relation to an altitude, height or cloud ceiling, it should be pronounced as:

    (a)   FOWER FIFE ZERO ZERO

    (b)   FOURTY FIFE HUNDRED

    (c)   FOWER TOUSAND FIFE HUNDRED

    (d)   FOWER FIFE HUNDRED

4. A recorded broadcast of meteorological reports for a group of aerodromes, transmitted on a dedicated frequency for use by aircraft in-flight, is known as:

    (a)   VOLMET

    (b)   ATIS

    (c)   LARS

    (d)   MATZ

5. A radio transmission described as 'Readability 4' is best described as:

    (a)   Readable now and then

    (b)   Readable but with difficulty

    (c)   Perfectly readable

    (d)   Readable

6. When making a standard 'overhead join' from 1000ft above the circuit height, at what point would the pilot commence the descent to circuit height and report 'descending dead side'?

    (a)   Once within the ATZ, but not within 500ft of circuit height until on the 'dead side'

    (b)   Once on the dead side of the runway, which is always the right-hand side

    (c)   Once on the dead side of the runway, turning in the same direction as the established circuit

    (d)   Over the 'live side' of the runway, whilst turning opposite to the established circuit direction

7.   The transponder code 7700 can be used to indicate:

(a)   A simulated emergency, as long as you have broadcast this intention to the ATSU

(b)   A simulated emergency, if in communication with an ATSU

(c)   A distress situation, if the pilot is not in direct communication with an ATSU

(d)   A radio failure

8.   The correct ATC phraseology meaning 'Confirm the code and mode set on the transponder' is:

(a)   Verify Squawk (code)

(b)   Confirm Squawk (code)

(c)   Squawk (code)

(d)   Reset Squawk (mode) (code)

9.   When should a pilot first use the phrase 'Take-off' in an RTF exchange?

(a)   When ready for take-off

(b)   After being cleared to line-up on an active runway

(c)   Only during an aborted take-off

(d)   In response to a clearance to take-off

10.   If a pilot hears a distress call, which is not answered by the ATSU, the most appropriate course of action is for the pilot to:

(a)   Maintain radio silence, then change to en-route frequency

(b)   Change frequency to the International Aeronautical Emergency Frequency and repeat the message exactly as received

(c)   Squawk 7700, maintain radio silence

(d)   Relay the distress message, making it clear that the aircraft relaying the message is not itself in distress

11.   Urgency is a condition where:

(a)   The aircraft is threatened by serious and/or imminent danger, and requires immediate assistance

(b)   There is a situation concerning the safety of an aircraft or other vehicle, or of some person on board or in sight, but not requiring immediate assistance

(c)   There is uncertainty of the flight's current status

(d)   It is expected that the aircraft will require assistance in the foreseeable future

12.   Which of the following best represents the order of information to be given in an emergency call:

(a)   Aircraft call sign/Name of station addressed/nature of emergency/intentions of pilot/position (inc. level and heading)/pilot qualification/other information/aircraft type

(b)   Name of station addressed/nature of emergency/position (inc. level and heading)/intentions of pilot/pilot qualification/other information/ Aircraft call sign/aircraft type

(c)   Aircraft call sign/aircraft type/Name of station addressed/nature of emergency/intentions of pilot/pilot qualification/position (inc. level and heading)/other information/

(d)   Name of station addressed/Aircraft call sign/aircraft type/nature of emergency/intentions of pilot/position (inc. level and heading)/pilot qualification/other information

1.   The correct phraseology for a pilot to use once the pre take-off checks have been completed and the aircraft is ready to take-off is:

   (a)   [Call sign] ready for take-off

   (b)   [Call sign] ready for departure

   (c)   [Call sign] take-off

   (d)   [Call sign] pre take-off checks complete

2.   A radio transmission that is classified as readability 2 is:

   (a)   Readable now and then

   (b)   Readable but with difficulty

   (c)   Unreadable

   (d)   Readable

3.   Where an ATSU permits a call sign to be abbreviated, the correct abbreviation of Thurston G-ASMY would be:

   (a)   Thurston MY

   (b)   Thurston G-MY

   (c)   Thurston G-ASMY

   (d)   Thurston Y

4.   If an ATSU wants a pilot to change frequency and listen out on that new frequency, the correct word or phrase to use is:

   (a)   QSY

   (b)   Monitor

   (c)   Freecall

   (d)   Break

5.   A pilot is in established communication with an ATSU, who have allocated a squawk (SSR code), when an emergency situation occurs. The pilot should notify this emergency condition by:

   (a)   Changing to 121.5MHz and making an emergency call

   (b)   Changing the squawk to 7000 whilst maintaining radio silence

   (c)   Making an emergency call on the frequency in use and initially maintaining the allocated SSR code

   (d)   Squawking 7700 whilst changing to 121.5MHz

6.   An aircraft is offered the clearance,

   "G-BD, after the A320 has crossed ahead of you, enter and backtrack 07"

   If the pilot chooses to accept the clearance, the correct response is:

   (a)   "Roger G-BD"

   (b)   "Wilco after the A320 G-BD"

   (c)   "Enter and backtrack 07, G-BD"

   (d)   "After the crossing A320, enter and backtrack 07, G-BD"

7. In which of the following circumstances might it be appropriate to request a Special VFR (SVFR) clearance?

   (a) To cross an ATZ in uncontrolled airspace when flying IFR

   (b) To cross a Class A airway in VMC

   (c) To cross a CTR, without landing at the controlling aerodrome, without contacting ATC

   (d) To operate in a CTR without complying with IFR

8. A flight is instructed to fly at a specified altitude. The correct pressure setting to use so that the altimeter indicates altitude is:

   (a) QNH

   (b) QFE

   (c) QDM

   (d) QSY

9. The magnetic bearing to a VDF station, or the magnetic heading to reach a VDF station assuming nil wind, is described in the 'Q' code as:

   (a) QNE

   (b) QDR

   (c) QTE

   (d) QDM

10. An ATC message in the form of:

    "*G-DCBA after departure route cleared directly to the zone boundary not above 2500ft, QNH 1005, squawk 4356*"

    Is:

    (a) A departure clearance, which automatically includes take-off clearance

    (b) A conditional clearance

    (c) A clearance to take-off, with further instructions to follow

    (d) A route clearance, this is NOT a take-off clearance

11. How may a flight plan be activated by a pilot whilst in flight?

    (a) By mobile telephone to the Parent ATSU

    (b) By requesting a radio relay to the destination airfield

    (c) By request on the appropriate FIS frequency

    (d) By selecting the pre-notified SSR code

12. The most appropriate way for obtaining pre-flight meteorological information is:

    (a) By requesting a met. briefing from an ATC officer

    (b) By self-briefing before flight using notified met. information sources

    (c) By accessing VOLMET for the departure airfield

    (d) By calling the appropriate FIS frequency

The 'readability' of a radio transmission can be classified in accordance with the table below:

Readability Scale	Definition
1	Unreadable
2	Readable now and then
3	Readable but with difficulty
4	Readable
5	Perfectly readable

Further Reference: PPL2>Communications>Departure Procedures>Radio Check

The essential purpose of standard phraseology in aviation communications is to avoid confusion and ambiguities. This is why so much emphasis is placed on only using recognised phraseology. In response to a query, the following responses are particularly inappropriate:

'ROGER'   This only means 'I have received all of your last transmission'

'CORRECT'   This only means 'True or accurate'

'WILCO'   This only means 'I have understood and will comply with your message'

It should be clear that using either of these replies to a question that simply requires a 'yes' (AFFIRM) or 'no' (NEGATIVE) response is almost certain to generate confusion and ambiguity

Further Reference: PPL2>Communications>Departure Procedures>Standard Phraseology

Once satisfactory two-way communication has been established with an ATSU, it is normal practice for both parties to drop the use of the ATSU call-sign and suffix in an ongoing exchange. However, an aircraft may only abbreviate its own call-sign after the ATSU has first done so.

Further Reference: PPL2>Communications>Call signs, Abbreviations, General Procedures>Call signs

The standard protocol is that when transmitting a radio frequency, all digits are pronounced, and the decimal place is indicated using the word 'decimal' (pronounced 'DAYSEEMAL').

Further Reference: PPL2>Communications>General Operating Procedures> Transmission of Numbers and Transmission of Time

Where an aircraft's transponder is fitted with Mode C, this mode will transmit the aircraft's flight level (based on 1013hPa). Some ATC units are able to process this information further and convert the screen display to show the aircraft's altitude based on the actual QNH. The ATC instruction "Confirm [level]" means that the pilot should check and confirm the aircraft's level, it is used to verify that the Mode C Flight Level / Altitude read-out the controller is seeing is within acceptable tolerances.

Further Reference: PPL2>Communications>En-route Procedures>Use of Transponder

When an ATSU invites a pilot flying en-route to "Pass your message", probably the most commonly used mnemonic for passing flight details is TP AIR:

T   aircraft **T**ype

P   Point of departure and destination, present **P**osition

A   **A**ltitude/height/flight level, with altimeter setting if appropriate

I   **I**ntentions i.e. estimate, routing, destination, flight rules (VFR/IFR) etc.

R   **R**equest – type of service required etc.

This mnemonic should provide all the information the controller needs; the controller will ask for further information if required.

Further Reference: PPL2>Communications>En-route Procedures>Establishing Contact – Passing Details

Because it is a single frequency serving many airfields, SAFETYCOM should only be used when at less than 2000ft above airfield elevation (or less than 1000ft above circuit level if applicable) and within 10nm of the airfield.

Further Reference: PPL2>Communications>Arrival/Traffic Pattern Procedures>RTF at Unattended Airfields

The table below summarises the three altimeter pressure settings, and the appropriate terminology. It is essential that there is no confusion between pilot and controller on this point, the pilot should always know what pressure setting is being used and how it represents the aircraft's vertical distance above the surface.

Altimeter Setting	Datum	Terminology
QFE	A fixed point on the surface	'Height'
QNH	Mean Sea Level	'Altitude'
Standard Setting	The 1013hPa pressure level	'Flight Level'

Further Reference: PPL2>Communications>En-Route Procedures>Level and Position Reporting

A pilot can request the aircraft's true bearing from a VDF station (in other words, the magnetic radial, corrected for variation), by using the 'Q' code QTE, or simply by requesting 'True Bearing'. The appropriate 'Q' codes to be used when requesting or confirming VDF information are:

QDM	The magnetic track **TO** the VDF station
QDR	The magnetic bearing **FROM** the VDF station
QTE	The true bearing **FROM** the VDF station

Further Reference: PPL2>Communications>En-Route Procedures>VHF Direction Finding (VDF)

A pilot wishing to enter a MATZ is advised to contact the controlling airfield at a range of 15nm, or a flying time of 5 minutes, from the MATZ boundary – whichever occurs sooner (ie is further away).

Further Reference: PPL2>Communications>En-route Procedures>MATZs

Communications paper 1 Q11   Answer D

Within the UK, student pilots who are flying solo should use the call sign prefix 'Student' on making initial contact with an ATSU, so that the Air Traffic Service can take into account the student pilot's more limited ability and experience when issuing information and/or instructions.

Further Reference: PPL2>Communications>Call signs, Abbreviations, General Procedures>Student Call sign

Communications paper 1 Q12   Answer B

The recognised categories of Emergency Message are Distress and Urgency.

Distress is a situation where the aircraft is threatened by serious and /or imminent danger and requires immediate assistance. A distress call takes precedence over all other radio messages.

Urgency is a situation concerning the safety of the aircraft, or another vessel, or person(s) on board or in sight, but which does not require immediate assistance. An urgency call takes precedence over all other radio messages except a distress call.

Further Reference: PPL2>Communications>Emergency Procedures>Priority of Messages

Communications paper 2 Q1   Answer C

The word 'ROGER' means that the speaker has received all of the last transmission – nothing more. There is no inference that the speaker has understood the message in any way, or has any intention of acting on it or complying with any instruction or clearance within it.

Further Reference: PPL2>Communications>Departure Procedures>Roger

Communications paper 2 Q2   Answer C

The phrase 'Disregard' simply means 'ignore'.

Further Reference: PPL2>Communications>En-route Procedures >Avoiding
                      Confusion

Communications paper 2 Q3   Answer C

When a number is transmitted in relation to altitude, height, cloud height, cloud ceiling and visibility, it is normally pronounced in thousands (TOUSAND) and hundreds (HUN DRED) of the relevant unit.

Further Reference: PPL2>Communications>General Operating Procedures>
                      Transmission of Numbers and Transmission of Time

Communications paper 2 Q4   Answer A

VOLMET is officially described as 'meteorological information for aircraft in flight'. In practice, VOLMET is a recorded broadcast of METARs for a group of airfields, normally broadcast in alphabetical order and covering a specific geographical region. This broadcast is intended to be received by aircraft in the 'en-route' (cruise) phase. Examples of VOLMET broadcasts include 'London South' 'Paris'; 'Frankfurt 1'; 'Dublin' etc

Further Reference: PPL2>Communications>En-route Procedures>VOLMET and ATIS

Communications paper 2 Q5   Answer D

The readability of a radio transmission can be 'graded' on a scale from 1 to 5 where 1 is unreadable and 5 is perfectly readable. Scale '4' means that the transmission is 'readable'

Further Reference: PPL2>Communications>departure Procedures >Radio Check

Answers TWO

Communications paper 2 Q6   Answer C

The standard over-head join is illustrated below. The 'descending' call is made once the aircraft has commenced its descent on the 'deadside'.

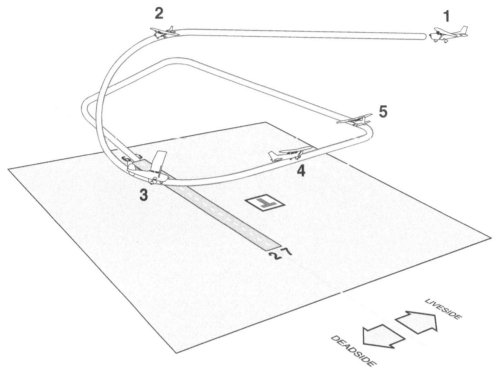

1   Approach airfield at 2,000 feet above airfield elevation or 1000ft above notified circuit level

2   Observe signals square and windsock, determine runway in use. If unable to do so, continue circling. Lookout for other aircraft. Maintain height until on 'deadside' Radio call "Overhead for runway xx"

3   Once on deadside, make a descending turn (in the circuit direction) to circuit height remaining on the deadside. Radio call if required, "Deadside descending"

4   Pass within the upwind end of the runway, level at circuit height

5   Join the circuit, maintain good lookout

Further Reference: PPL2>Communications>Arrival/Traffic Pattern Procedures>Circuit Joining and Overhead Joins

Communications paper 2 Q7   Answer C

The transponder code 7700 indicates an emergency, but should only be used in the first instance if the pilot is not in direct communication with an ATSU and if no other ATC-allocated squawk is in use.

If the pilot is already in communication with an ATSU when an emergency arises, the appropriate emergency call should be made, and in due course the ATSU will advise if the squawk should be changed.

Further Reference: PPL2>Communications>En-Route Procedures>Use of Transponder
                       PPL2>Communications>Emergency Procedures>Distress/Urgency Calls

Communications paper 2 Q8   Answer B

The full set of Secondary Surveillance Radar phrases and their meanings should be memorised:

Standard Phraseology	Meaning
Squawk (code and mode)	Set this mode and code
Squawk standby	Set the transponder to the standby position
Squawk Charlie	Set the transponder to mode C
Squawk ident	Operate the ident button on the transponder
Confirm squawk (code)	Confirm the code and mode set on the transponder
Reset Squawk (mode)(code)	Set the transponder to standby, then re-select the assigned code and mode
Confirm (level)	Check and confirm your level (used to verify the Mode C flight level/altitude read-out the controller is seeing)

SSR operating instructions require a read back from the pilot.

Further Reference: PPL2>Communications>En-route Procedures>Use of Transponder

Communications paper 2 Q9   Answer D

The phrase "take-off" will first be used by the ATSU, the pilot only uses the phrase 'take-off' to acknowledge an instruction or clearance to take-off.

Further Reference: PPL2>Communications>Departure Procedures>Taxying
                       Instructions, Holding Instructions, Take-off Instructions

Communications paper 2 Q10   Answer D

If an aircraft hears an emergency message, which is not answered by the ATSU on frequency, the correct action is to relay the emergency message to the ATSU, whilst making it clear that the 'relaying' aircraft is not the aircraft with an emergency.

Further Reference: PPL2>Communications>Emergency Procedures>relay of Emergency
                       Messages

Communications paper 2 Q11   Answer B

The definitions of Urgency and Distress are given in full at the 'Essential Revision' section.

Further Reference: PPL2>Communications>Emergency Procedures>Distress/Urgency
                       Calls

Communications paper 2 Q12   Answer D

The recommended format of an emergency call is given in the 'Essential Revision' section.

Further Reference: PPL2>Communications>Emergency Procedures>Distress/Urgency
                       Calls

Answers TWO

Communications **Paper THREE Answers**

After completing the pre-take-off checks satisfactorily, the pilot reports that the aircraft is ready to depart. The phraseology used is "[call sign] ready for departure". The words 'take-off' are not used at this stage. Once a pilot has reported ready for departure, and if the ATSU knows of no reason why the aircraft should not depart, the words "take-off" can be used for the first time, by the ATSU. The phrase "take-off" will first be used by the ATSU, not the pilot.

Further Reference: PPL2>Communications>Departure Procedures>Taxying Instructions, Holding Instructions, Take-off Instructions

Communications paper 3 Q2   Answer A

The table of the 'readability' of a radio transmission is given in the 'Essential Revision' section.

Further Reference: PPL2>Communications>Departure Procedures>Radio Check

Communications paper 3 Q3   Answer A

This call sign can be abbreviated in accordance with the table given in the essential Revision section.

Further Reference: PPL2>Communications>Call signs, Abbreviations, General Procedures>Call signs

Communications paper 3 Q4   Answer B

The full set of phraseology is given in the Essential Revision section.

Further Reference: PPL2>Communications>En-route Procedures>Standard Phraseology

Communications paper 3 Q5   Answer C

Where a pilot is already in communication with an ATSU, an emergency call should be made on the frequency in use. In the same way, if an aircraft already has an allocated SSR code (squawk) this should be retained, at least initially.

Further Reference: PPL2>Communications>Emergency Procedures>Emergency Frequencies
PPL2>Communications>Emergency Procedures>Distress/Urgency Calls

Communications paper 3 Q6   Answer D

The ATC message is a conditional clearance in the form of:

'Aircraft call sign/the condition/the identity of the condition object/the instruction'

On choosing to accept the condition clearance, the pilot reads it back in the same order, with the only modification being to put the call sign at the end of the message, hence:

'The condition/the identity of the condition object/the instruction/ aircraft call sign'

Further Reference: PPL2>Communications>Departure Procedures>Conditional Clearances

Communications paper 3 Q7   Answer D

A Special VFR (SVFR) clearance allows a flight to operate in a control zone (CTR) without complying with Instrument Flight Rules (IFR), but in weather conditions which do not meet the Visual Meteorological Conditions (VMC) criteria specified for that class of airspace. To obtain a SVFR clearance it is necessary to contact the appropriate ATSU before entering the CTR. Note that a class A airway is a control area (CTA), and SVFR is NOT permitted in a class A CTA.

Further Reference: PPL2>Air Law>Division of Airspace and Air Traffic Services>Special VFR

Communications paper 3 Q8   Answer A

The altimeter settings and associated terminology are summarised below.

Altimeter Setting	Datum	Terminology
QFE	A fixed point on the surface	'Height'
QNH	Mean Sea Level	'Altitude'
Standard Setting	The 1013hPa pressure level	'Flight Level'

Further Reference: PPL2>Communications>En-Route Procedures>Level and Position
                                Reporting

Communications paper 3 Q9   Answer D

In relation to VHF Direction Finding (VDF), 'QDM' is defined as the magnetic heading to
be steered by the aircraft (assuming no wind) to reach the VDF station. The Q codes are
explained more fully in the 'Essential Revision' section.

Further Reference: PPL2>Communications>En-route Procedures>VHF Direction
                                Finding (VDF)

Communications paper 3 Q10   Answer D

An ATC route clearance may often be in the format of a departure clearance, a set of
instructions giving a route (and level and squawk instructions) to be followed AFTER
departure. An ATC route clearance is **NOT** an instruction to take-off or enter an active
runway.

Further Reference: PPL2>Communications>Departure Procedures>Departure
                                Clearance/Departure Instructions

Communications paper 3 Q11   Answer C

A flight plan can be activated after departure (typically from an airfield without an ATC or
AFIS unit) by contacting an ATSU and requesting activation of the flight plan. Typically this
is done on the appropriate FIS frequency, although busy RTF frequencies should be avoided.

Further Reference: PPL2>Air Law>Rules of the Air and Air Traffic Services>Flight Plans

Communications paper 3 Q12   Answer B

The 'official' sources of meteorological information are 'notified' in the AIP. In relation to
the other answer options, ATC officers do not necessarily have any met. qualifications
and are unlikely to be met. forecasters. VOLMET is unlikely to be accessed from the
ground and only gives actual weather conditions. It is unlikely that an FIS controller can
be contacted whilst the aircraft is on the ground.

Further Reference: PPL2>Air Law>The Aeronautical Information Service>
                                Meteorology

Intentionally Left Blank

	Paper 1					Paper 2					Paper 3			
	A	B	C	D		A	B	C	D		A	B	C	D
1	☐	☐	☐	☐	1	☐	☐	☐	☐	1	☐	☐	☐	☐
2	☐	☐	☐	☐	2	☐	☐	☐	☐	2	☐	☐	☐	☐
3	☐	☐	☐	☐	3	☐	☐	☐	☐	3	☐	☐	☐	☐
4	☐	☐	☐	☐	4	☐	☐	☐	☐	4	☐	☐	☐	☐
5	☐	☐	☐	☐	5	☐	☐	☐	☐	5	☐	☐	☐	☐
6	☐	☐	☐	☐	6	☐	☐	☐	☐	6	☐	☐	☐	☐
7	☐	☐	☐	☐	7	☐	☐	☐	☐	7	☐	☐	☐	☐
8	☐	☐	☐	☐	8	☐	☐	☐	☐	8	☐	☐	☐	☐
9	☐	☐	☐	☐	9	☐	☐	☐	☐	9	☐	☐	☐	☐
10	☐	☐	☐	☐	10	☐	☐	☐	☐	10	☐	☐	☐	☐
11	☐	☐	☐	☐	11	☐	☐	☐	☐	11	☐	☐	☐	☐
12	☐	☐	☐	☐	12	☐	☐	☐	☐	12	☐	☐	☐	☐

Intentionally Left Blank

Intentionally Left Blank

Intentionally Left Blank